INVENTORS AND INVENTIONS

by
Joanna Brundle

Photo Credits

Images are courtesy of Shutterstock.com. With thanks to Getty Images, Thinkstock Photo and iStockphoto.

Cover – Midnight Studio, 2 – Vintage Tone, 4&5 – Everett Historical, fotosullenuvole, I Believe I Can Fly, 6&7 – Imfoto, Jacek Chabraszewski, Michael Stokes, mahey, 8&9 – vasabii, Africa Studio, mama_mia, 10&11 – serato, HDesert, meirion matthais, Everett – Art, Orange Deer studio, 12&13 – Everett Historical, Prachaya, Roekdeethaweesab, Pero Mihajlovic, tfhrc.gov, Pushish Images, BakerJarvis, James S. Davies, SkillUp, Pangog200, Nattakit.K, 14&15 – Glen Bowman, tlindsayg, Artem Shadrin, wavebreakmedia, 16&17 – Bjoern Wylezich, Thawornnurak, JPC–PROD, David Ryo, 18&19 – Fae, yoshi0511, Kwangmoozaa, 20&21 – ImagingL, wavebreakmedia, drserg, Melody Smart, 22&23 – yvontrep, Yutthaphong, David Peter Robinson, EMFA16, 24&25 – Africa Studio, Dusan Petkovic, A Daily Odyssey, Acroterion, 26&27 – Swtpc6800, Zoeytoja, Kateryna Kon, Roger Utting, 28&29 – Andy Shell, rocharibeiro, Elena Nichzhenova, 30 – Dmytro Zinkevych.

BookLife
PUBLISHING

©2021
BookLife Publishing Ltd.
King's Lynn
Norfolk PE30 4LS

ISBN: 978-1-78637-145-8

Written by:
Joanna Brundle

Edited by:
William Anthony

Designed by:
Gareth Liddington

CONTENTS

Words in **bold** are explained in the glossary on page 31.

INCREDIBLE
INVENTIONS

Inventions are completely new objects, machines, **processes** or products. The people who have the ideas and create these inventions are called inventors. Some inventions make our lives easier or more enjoyable. Others keep us safe or help us to **communicate** with one another. Look around you now. Everything you see, from paper to computers, has been invented by someone who had a clever idea. Successful inventions, such as television, radio and the aeroplane, often change our lives completely.

IN 1903, THE WRIGHT BROTHERS INVENTED AN AEROPLANE CALLED THE WRIGHT FLYER THAT ACHIEVED THE FIRST POWERED, CONTROLLED FLIGHT.

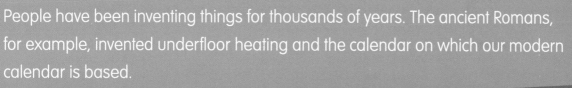

People have been inventing things for thousands of years. The ancient Romans, for example, invented underfloor heating and the calendar on which our modern calendar is based.

Some inventors spend years working on their ideas. Inventor James Dyson took 15 years and 5,127 attempts to produce a vacuum cleaner that was good enough to sell. Some inventions happen by accident. Post-it notes stick to surfaces but can be peeled off again. The weak glue that allows them to do this was invented by Spencer Silver, who was actually trying to make a super-sticky glue.

Wigs were invented by the ancient Egyptians.

LET'S GET MOVING

As you travel around, have you ever thought about all the inventions that have made bicycle, car, train or aeroplane journeys possible? The wheel, for example, was invented over 5,500 years ago and changed the world of transport forever.

BICYCLES

PENNY-FARTHING

MOUNTAIN BIKE

In 1871, inventor James Starley created a version of the penny-farthing bicycle. In 1875, his nephew invented his 'safety bicycle' with wheels that matched each other in size, and a chain. Lightweight mountain bikes were invented in the 1970s.

MOTOR CARS

The first car powered by petrol had three wheels and was invented by Karl Benz in 1886. Later in that very same year, Gottlieb Daimler invented the first four-wheeled motor car.

'Bigfoot' was the name given to a **monster truck** invented by Bob Chandler in the 1970s. Monster truck shows now attract thousands of spectators.

Some inventions have made cars safer. Windscreen wipers were invented in 1903 by Mary Anderson. The idea came to her on a snowy car journey when her driver had to keep stopping to clear snow from the screen.

HOME SWEET HOME

Many inventions, from the light bulb to the lawnmower, have made life at home easier.

LIGHT BULBS

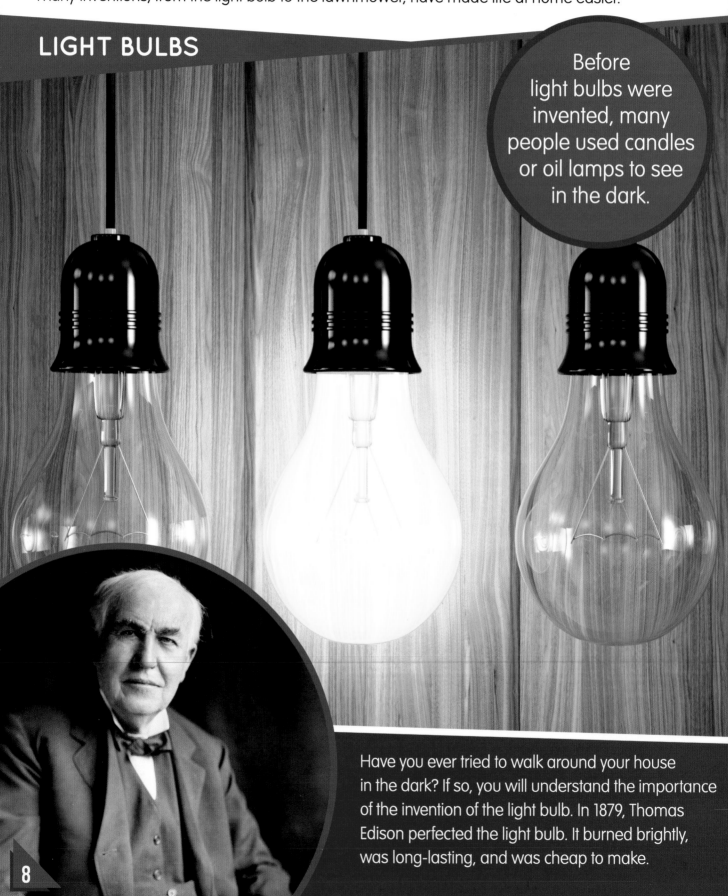

Before light bulbs were invented, many people used candles or oil lamps to see in the dark.

Have you ever tried to walk around your house in the dark? If so, you will understand the importance of the invention of the light bulb. In 1879, Thomas Edison perfected the light bulb. It burned brightly, was long-lasting, and was cheap to make.

DISHWASHERS

The first **automatic** dishwashing machine was invented by Josephine Cochrane in 1887. Powered by a motor or by hand, the machine sprayed soapy hot water over dirty dishes, then fresh water to rinse them. The first electric dishwashers appeared in the 1920s.

POP-UP TOASTERS

It's easy to burn toast under a grill. In 1919, factory worker Charles Strite invented something to solve the problem – a pop-up toaster. It toasted both sides of the bread at once and, thanks to a timer and springs, it popped the toast up when it was ready.

LAWNMOWERS

The lawnmower was invented in 1830 by Edwin Budding. Budding worked in a **cotton mill** and had been asked to make a machine that could trim unwanted tufts from fabric. This gave him the idea for a lawnmower that could cut grass quickly and easily.

Before Budding invented the lawnmower, people cut lawns with a long, curved blade called a scythe.

DISPOSABLE NAPPIES

In 1947, Valerie Hunter Gordon began making **disposable nappies** – nappies that you can throw away after one use – for her own children. She used cotton wool with a cover made from old nylon parachutes. Her idea was developed in the 1950s by Victor Mills and all-in-one disposable nappies were soon sold in shops.

FLUSHING TOILETS

Ancient civilisations, including the Romans and the Indus Valley, used running water to flush away waste. In 1596, the godson of Queen Elizabeth I, Sir John Harrington, invented a toilet called a water closet for her. The idea did not catch on and people continued using holes in the ground or chamber pots, which they emptied out of their windows.

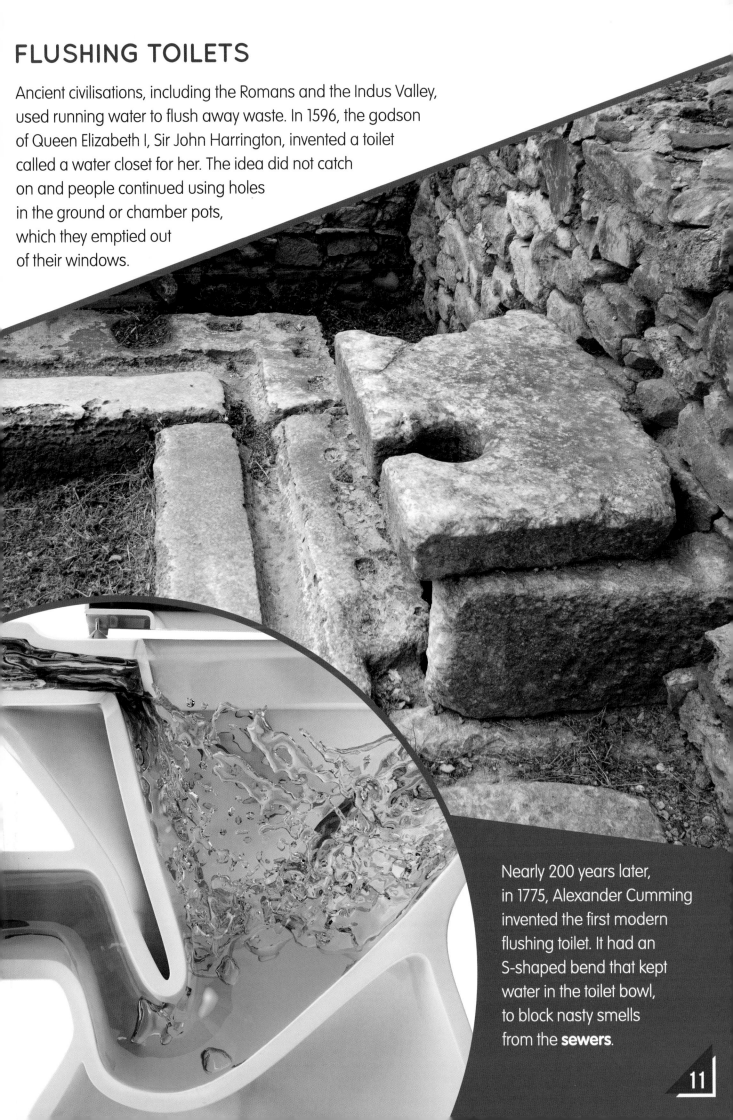

Nearly 200 years later, in 1775, Alexander Cumming invented the first modern flushing toilet. It had an S-shaped bend that kept water in the toilet bowl, to block nasty smells from the **sewers**.

BRILLIANT MINDS

Some inventors stand out from the rest because of the brilliance of their inventions or the huge number of things they invented.

LEONARDO DA VINCI (1452–1519)

- Invented a huge range of machines including an automaton (robot) in 1495
- Drew designs and models that proved workable hundreds of years later, for example a parachute, helicopter, diving equipment and a winged flying machine

GALILEO GALILEI (1564–1642)

- Invented a powerful telescope that allowed him to look at the Moon and prove that the Earth and other planets **orbit** the Sun

ALEXANDER GRAHAM BELL (1847–1922)

- Received a **patent** for the telephone in 1876, narrowly beating another inventor, Elisha Gray

THOMAS EDISON (1847–1931)

- Inventions included the light bulb and the phonograph, which played back recorded sounds
- Held a world record of 1,093 patents

GARRETT MORGAN (1877–1963)

- Invented the three-light traffic light, making driving safer for future drivers

GRACE HOPPER (1906–1992)

- Invented a piece of **software** that could translate instructions into code for computers to read, which changed the way computers worked

DEEPIKA KURUP (BORN 1998)

- Invented a **water-purification** system that is renewable, **solar-powered** and doesn't cost too much money to use, and could bring clean drinking water to people around the world

FOOD FOR
THOUGHT

Inventors and their inventions have given us a huge range of foods to enjoy.

CHOCOLATE

At first, chocolate was only enjoyed as a drink. However, in 1847, **confectioner** Joseph Fry invented something that is still well-loved today. He mixed sugar with cocoa butter and cocoa powder and pressed the mixture into moulds to make the first chocolate bars. The first Easter eggs followed in 1873.

In 1866, Fry's Chocolate Cream became the world's first **mass-produced** chocolate bar.

CHOCOLATE CHIP COOKIES

Chocolate chip cookies were invented by accident in 1938 by Ruth Wakefield. She had run out of cocoa powder while making cookies and used broken chunks of chocolate instead. The short baking time meant that the chunks did not melt.

TINNED FOOD

In 1809, Nicholas Appert invented a way to seal food inside a bottle or jar to keep it fresh.
In 1810, Peter Durand patented the use of tin-coated food cans, instead of bottles.

THE TIN OPENER WAS NOT INVENTED UNTIL 1858 — THE FIRST CANS HAD TO BE OPENED WITH A HAMMER AND CHISEL.

FROZEN FOOD

Clarence Birdseye discovered that food that was frozen very quickly at very low temperatures still looked and tasted good when it was defrosted. In the 1920s, he invented a way of fast-freezing foods such as fish, fruit and vegetables.

Clarence Birdseye's invention helps to feed millions of people every day.

COMMUNICATION

STAMPS

Before telephones and email were invented, people had to write letters to communicate with one another. Unlike today, the person receiving the letter had to pay. In 1837, Rowland Hill invented a sticky stamp that was paid for by the person sending the letter. The first stamps went on sale in May, 1840, and cost one penny.

The stamps were printed in black ink and became known as Penny Blacks.

MOBILE PHONES

The first handheld mobile phone was invented by Martin Cooper. It was launched in 1984 and, because it was so big and heavy, it soon became known as 'The Brick'.

BALLPOINT PENS

Ballpoint pens were invented in the 1930s by newspaper journalist László Bíró. Bíró noticed that the ink used to print newspapers dried quickly without smudging, unlike the ink used in other pens. He invented a pen with a tiny ball bearing in the end, which spread the quick-drying ink as it turned.

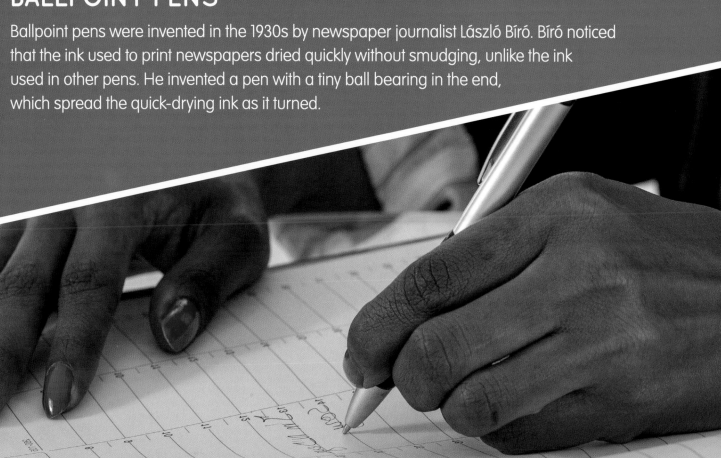

GEL PENS

Gel pens were invented by a Japanese company called Sakura. The gel they contain is water-based and comes in lots of colours. The first gel pens went on sale in 1984.

PICTURE PERFECT

Digital cameras were invented in 1975 by Steve Sasson. The first one weighed a whopping 3.6 kilograms (kg).

In the early 1800s, Joseph Nicéphore Niépce began to experiment with photography, which he called heliography. A photograph taken by him around 1826 is thought to be the oldest surviving photograph. During the 1830s, William Henry Fox Talbot began inventing a process that meant a photograph could be printed again and again. In 1883, George Eastman invented rolls of camera film and in 1888, his first camera, which he called the 'Kodak Black', went on sale, bringing photography to all.

TELEVISION

Today, most homes have at least one television. In 1924, John Logie Baird became the first person to build a working mechanical TV. In 1926, he gave the first public demonstration of black-and-white moving pictures on a TV. Electronic TVs, which gave bigger, clearer pictures, appeared in the late 1920s and, by the early 1960s, there were TVs in millions of homes. The first colour TVs went on sale in the 1950s, but few people could afford to buy one.

Today, the television has become a machine you can access the internet on and even control with your voice!

THE INTERNET AND THE
WORLD WIDE WEB

A series of computers all linked together is called a network. The internet is a giant network of computers that 'talk' to each other and share information. It began in 1969 as a network of just four university computers in the US, called ARPANET.

The first email was sent using ARPANET in 1971 by Ray Tomlinson, who also invented the @ sign in email addresses. Many computer scientists and engineers helped to develop the internet. Today, we all use the internet for information, entertainment and learning.

Computer scientist Tim Berners-Lee developed a system that allowed people at his workplace to share information. He soon realised that a worldwide network of computers would allow people around the world to share information.

TIM BERNERS-LEE

The first webpage appeared in 1991. It gave information about how to post and search webpages.

A new computer language called HTML was used to create electronic documents called pages. These pages could be sent and received according to a set of rules called HTTP. Tim Berners-Lee first called his invention 'Information Mesh', but this was soon changed to the 'World Wide Web'.

HMTL CODE

HEALTH AND
SAFETY

Many inventions have helped us to live healthier, safer lives.

SAFETY PINS

Safety pins were invented in 1849 by Walter Hunt, while fiddling with a piece of wire. He coiled the wire into a spring, which allowed a sharp point at one end to be forced into a clasp. The clasp stopped the pin from pricking the user.

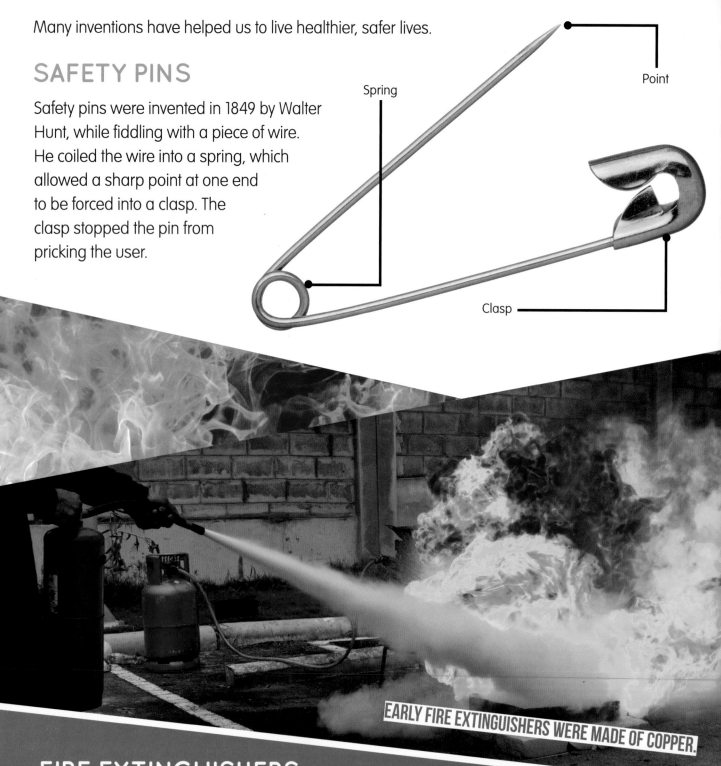

Point

Spring

Clasp

EARLY FIRE EXTINGUISHERS WERE MADE OF COPPER.

FIRE EXTINGUISHERS

The modern, portable fire extinguisher was invented around 1817 by George William Manby. An extinguisher patented by Ambrose Godfrey, almost 100 years before, used exploding gunpowder to scatter fire-extinguishing liquid!

ZEBRA CROSSINGS

As the number of cars on the road grew in the 1930s, it became important to provide safe places for people to cross. The government experimented with differently coloured markings, eventually introducing black and white stripes in 1951. James Callaghan **MP** is thought to have come up with the name 'zebra crossing' while looking at the experimental markings in 1948.

Shaw's reflecting road studs, called cat's eyes, are used all around the world.

CAT'S EYES

On a dark car journey in 1933, Percy Shaw saw his headlights reflected in the eyes of a cat. He realised that reflecting road studs could improve road safety and in 1934, patented his invention.

ACCIDENTAL
INVENTIONS

CORNFLAKES

Cornflakes were invented when John and Will Kellogg accidentally left boiled wheat to go stale. Rather than waste it, they passed it through rollers, hoping to make a sheet of dough. Instead they got flakes. They then experimented with other grains, including corn. The flakes were very popular.

VELCRO

George de Mestral invented Velcro and introduced it to the world in 1955. The prickly heads of certain plants had got stuck on his trousers and in his dog's fur during a walk. After examining hooks on the plants under a **microscope**, he invented a hook and loop fastener for fabrics.

VELCRO IS USED TO FASTEN SHOES AND CLOTHES.

Today, better technology has helped us to make microwave ovens that are much smaller than the one built by Spencer.

24
Radar Range

MICROWAVE OVENS

An engineer named Percy Spencer was working on magnetrons (devices that give off **microwaves**) in 1945, when he noticed that a peanut bar in his pocket had started to cook. He then experimented with popcorn and an egg, both of which exploded. Realising that the food had been quickly cooked from the inside by the microwaves, he patented the first working microwave oven. It went into production in 1946. It was huge, weighing over 300 kg and standing 1.8 metres tall.

WEIRD AND WACKY
INVENTIONS

While some inventions are inspiring and life-changing, others are simply weird and wacky. A car exhaust that grills food for you as you travel, a device for taking your goldfish for a walk and tiny umbrellas for your shoes are some of the strangest.

THE RADIO HAT

SEE NEW DESIGN

The 'Man from Mars Radio Hat' was designed in 1949 by Victor T Hoeflich. In the days before portable speakers, this hat allowed the wearer to listen to music anywhere.

The anti-theft lunch bag is a clear plastic bag printed with a picture of mould. It makes the sandwich inside look mouldy so that nobody will want to steal it.

The Sinclair C5 was an electric vehicle for one person, launched in 1985. It was claimed that the C5 would change transport forever, but it turned out to be a spectacular failure. It gave no protection from the weather and people did not feel safe driving it.

Although it was a failure, the C5 made people begin to think about non-polluting electric vehicles.

YOUNG INVENTORS

Many inventions were created by young people.

LOUIS BRAILLE

An accident blinded Louis Braille as a young child. By 1824, at the age of just 15, he had worked out a system of reading and writing for blind people. The system, known as braille, uses six raised dots arranged in different patterns to represent the letters of the alphabet. Rather than seeing the letters, a blind person uses their fingertips to feel the dots. Braille published his system in 1829 and soon also developed it to cover mathematics, musical notes and other symbols.

Braille can be written by hand using a stylus and slate or by a machine.

GEORGE NISSEN

In 1930, teenage gymnast and swimmer George Nissen watched circus trapeze artists bounce into a safety net. He thought that if the net could be made bouncier, it could be used to perform somersaults, flips and other tricks. Using his parents' garage as a workshop, he strapped a canvas sheet to a steel frame. To give it more bounce, he connected the sheet to the frame using the inner tubes of tyres, later replaced by springs. Nissen first called his invention a bouncing rig, before changing the name to 'trampoline'.

Since Nissen invented the trampoline, trampolining has become a worldwide sport that even features in the **Olympic Games**.

LET'S INVENT

The current world record for inventions is 11,353, held by Shunpei Yamazaki of Japan. For inventors like Yamazaki, it all starts with just one good idea. Maybe you have a great idea for a clever invention too, like a machine that feeds you your breakfast in bed?

You don't have to wait until you are a grown-up to start inventing. Write a description of your invention, remembering to say how it will work and how it will be made. Draw a picture and add labels. Don't forget to think up a catchy name!

GLOSSARY

automatic	able to work without being controlled by a human
communicate	to pass information between two or more people
confectioner	a person who makes sweets and chocolate
cotton mill	a factory for spinning and weaving cotton fabrics
disposable nappies	nappies that, instead of being washed and re-used, are used once and then thrown away
journalist	a person who writes news reports for newspapers, magazines, radio, television or news websites
mass-produced	made in large quantities in factories, using mechanical processes
microscope	a piece of scientific equipment that makes things look many times bigger
microwaves	a type of energy wave
monster truck	a very large pickup truck with huge, chunky tyres
MP	a member of parliament, chosen by voters to represent a particular part of the United Kingdom
Olympic Games	an international sporting event, held every four years
orbit	move around a star or planet in a curved path
patent	a licence granted by the government, giving an inventor the right to make, use or sell an invention and stopping anyone else from doing so
processes	a set of actions that produce something or that lead to a particular result
sewers	underground pipes for carrying away waste
software	computer programs
solar-powered	uses energy from the Sun
water-purification	removing things from dirty water to make the water clean and safe enough to drink

INDEX